MORE BIZARRO

BY DAN PIRARO.

GRUB STREET LONDON

Published by Grub Street 1990
The Basement, 10 Chivalry Road
London SW11 1HT

Copyright 1990 by Chronicle Publishing Company
First published by Chronicle Books, San Francisco, California

British Library Cataloguing in Publication Data
Piraro, Dan
More Bizarro.
1. American humorous cartoons
I. Title
741.5973
ISBN 0-948817-35-6

Printed and bound in Great Britain
by Richard Clay Ltd

ALL TOLD, THIS IS THE EIGHTH BOOK OF MY CARTOONS PUBLISHED,
AND ALL ARE DEDICATED TO MY WIFE, KALIN. SHE'S A WONDERFUL
PERSON, VERY BRIGHT AND WITTY, LOTS OF FUN TO BE WITH,
AND LARGELY RESPONSIBLE FOR MY NOT BEING DEPRESSED AND
DISFUNCTIONAL ANYMORE.

WE MARRIED YOUNG, FOR NO REASON, AGAINST MOST
EVERYONE'S BETTER JUDGEMENT, ACTING ENTIRELY OUT OF A SORT
OF INSTINCT. I CAN'T SPEAK FOR HER, BUT IT HAS PROVEN TO BE
THE SMARTEST THING I EVER DID. AND SO, IN KEEPING WITH
TRADITION, THIS BOOK IS DEDICATED TO HER. WITH THE
EXCEPTION OF THE DRAWINGS OF PEOPLE WITH GLASSES,
WHICH ARE DEDICATED TO ELVIS COSTELLO, WHOSE LYRICS
I HAVE ALWAYS GREATLY ADMIRED.

THE CARTOONS OF DAN PIRARO VIRTUALLY DEFY CATEGORIZATION. AT ONCE NIHILISTIC AND REJOICEFUL, HE ATTEMPTS TO ANSWER THE TOUGH QUESTIONS, TO ADDRESS THE BURNING ISSUES OF OUR TIME. SINCE OXYGEN IS INVISIBLE, CAN WE EVER BE TRULY CERTAIN IT IS NOT MAKING FUN OF US? WAS SATAN'S CHOICE TO APPEAR TO EVE AS A SERPENT INSTEAD OF THE MORE LOGICAL CHOICE OF A POODLE PROVIDENTIAL? WHAT DO THE PEOPLE NEXT DOOR LOOK LIKE NAKED?

PIRARO WAS BORN IN THE LATTER HALF OF THE TWENTIETH CENTURY TO A ~~ATTRACTIVE~~ MID-TWENTIETH CENTURY COUPLE. THIS UNLIKELY COMBINATION OF CHRONOLOGY COUPLED WITH HIS "VIRTUALLY HAIRLESS PHYSICAL CONDITION" AT BIRTH CONTRIBUTE TO HIS BELIEF THAT HE IS THE MAN NOSTRADOMUS PROPHESIED ABOUT: "WHEN ~~TH~~ THE WIGGLY PINK INFANT CRIES OUT FOR HIS FUR, A WISE GUY WILL EMERGE WITH AMPLE PROBOSCIS." THESE WORDS DO SEEM TO EXPLAIN PIRARO'S CURIOUSLY LOYAL INTERNATIONAL FOLLOWING OF INTELLECTUALS, ELITISTS AND SPIRITUALLY BEREFT.

NOW WITH SOMETHING LESS THAN 400 MILLION READERS DAILY, BIZARRO CONTINUES TO BE THE MOST WIDELY READ SINGLE PANEL CARTOON OF THAT NAME.

Newton vs. Golden Delicious.

WE'VE THROWN OUT ALL THE BAGGAGE AND WE'RE STILL TOO HEAVY! IS THERE ANYTHING ELSE WE CAN DO WITHOUT!?
PIRARO

HELLO, ROY. YOU PROBABLY DON'T RECOGNIZE ME, I'M YOUR AMBITION. I GAVE UP ON YOU YEARS AGO, WHICH IS WHY YOU'RE SUCH A SLOB.
SO WHAT'S YOUR POINT?
PIRARO.

WE'RE OUTSIDE THE HOME OF SOME PEOPLE WHO'VE JUST EXPERIENCED A GRAVE PERSONAL TRAGEDY TO BADGER AND HARASS THEM FOR THE SAKE OF A FEW RATINGS POINTS. LET'S WATCH.....
PIRARO.